WHSmith

Revise

Maths and English

KS2: YEAR 3

Age 7–8

**Paul Broadbent,
Peter Patilla and
Louis Fidge**

First published 2007
exclusively for WHSmith by
Hodder Murray, a member of the Hodder Headline group
338 Euston Road
London
NW1 3BH

Impression number   10 9 8 7 6 5 4 3 2 1
Year   2008 2007
Text and illustrations © Hodder Education 2007

A CIP record for this book is available from the British Library.

Cover illustration by Sally Newton Illustrations

Typeset by Fakenham Photosetting Limited, Fakenham, Norfolk

ISBN – 13   978 0 34094271 0

Printed and bound in Italy.

Contents

Maths

English

The *WHS Revise* series

The *WHS Revise* books enable you to help your child revise and practise important skills taught in school. These skills form part of the National Curriculum and will help your child to improve his or her Maths and English.

Testing in schools

During their time at school all children will undergo a variety of tests. Regular testing is a feature of all schools. It is carried out:

● *informally* – in everyday classroom activities your child's teacher is continually assessing and observing your child's performance in a general way

● *formally* – more regular formal testing helps the teacher check your child's progress in specific areas.

Testing is important because:

● it provides evidence of your child's achievement and progress

● it helps the teacher decide which skills to focus on with your child

● it helps compare how different children are progressing.

The importance of revision

Regular revision is important to ensure your child remembers and practises skills he or she has been taught. These books will help your child revise and test his or her knowledge of some of the things he or she will be expected to know. They will help you prepare your child to be in a better position to face tests in school with confidence.

How to use this book

Units

Each book is divided into a Maths section and an English section. Within each section there are twenty units, each focusing on one key skill. Each unit begins with a **Remember** section, which introduces and revises essential information about the particular skill covered. If possible, read and discuss this with your child to ensure he or she understands it.

This is followed by a **Have a go** section, which contains a number of activities to help your child revise the topic thoroughly and use the skill effectively. Usually, your child should be able to do these activities fairly independently.

Revision tests

There are two revision tests at the end of the Maths section and two revision tests at the end of the English section. These test the skills covered in the preceding units and assess your child's progress and understanding. They can be marked by you or by your child. Your child should fill in his or her test score for each test in the space provided. This will provide a visual record of your child's progress and an instant sense of confidence and achievement.

Parents' notes

The parents' notes (on pages 30–31 for the Maths section and pages 59–60 for the English section) provide you with brief information on each skill and explain why it is important.

Answers

Answers to the unit questions and tests may be found on pages 32–34 (Maths) and pages 61–64 (English).

Unit 1: Place value

Remember

The **position of a digit** in a number gives its value.

8 tens

585 = 500 + 80 + 5

5 hundreds   5 ones

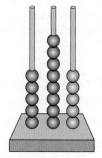

This abacus shows the number 585.

Have a go

Each abacus is having some beads added. Write the new number for each abacus.

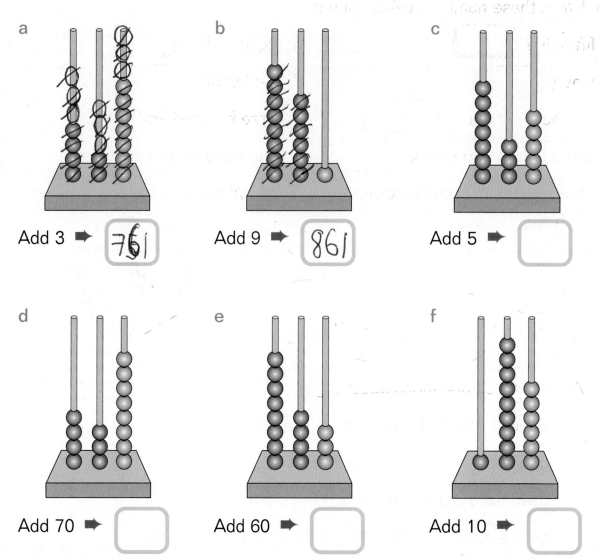

a

Add 3 ➡ 761

b

Add 9 ➡ 861

c

Add 5 ➡

d

Add 70 ➡

e

Add 60 ➡

f

Add 10 ➡

Unit 2: Reading and writing numbers

Remember

We use these words when talking about numbers.

Digit
There are only 10 digits
– 0 1 2 3 4 5 6 7 8 and
9. Digits are used to
build up longer numbers.
56 uses 2 digits
705 uses 3 digits

Numeral
A numeral is a symbol or
name for a number.

three   3   III

Figure
Figures are symbols
used to stand for whole
numbers.
Fifty-six in figures is 56.

Have a go

1 Write these numbers using figures.

a fifty-nine ☐

b eighty-three ☐

c ninety ☐

d five hundred ☐

e one hundred and six ☐

f three hundred and sixty ☐

g two hundred and twelve ☐

h nine hundred and sixty-two ☐

2 Look at the Roman numerals on the clock. Write these numerals using
figures.

a V ☐

b III ☐

c X ☐

d XII ☐

e VII ☐

f IX ☐

3 Answer these questions about digits.

a 375 Which of these digits is worth the most? _____

b 739 Which of these digits is worth the least? _____

c 455 How many digits are in the number? _____

d Arrange the digits 2, 6 and 4 to make the largest number. ____ ____ ____

e Arrange the digits 4, 3 and 7 to make the smallest number. ____ ____ ____

Unit 3: Multiples

Remember

Multiples are like tables.

The multiples of 2 are 2, 4, 6, 8, 10, 12, . . .
The multiples of 5 are 5, 10, 15, 20, 25, . . .

Multiples do not stop at the 10th, they go on and on.

The 100th multiple of 2 is 200.

Have a go

1 Continue these multiples.

a  These are multiples of ☐

b These are multiples of ☐

c These are multiples of ☐

2 Answer these questions about multiples.

a What is the 11th multiple of 2? ____   b What is the 50th multiple of 2? ____

c What is the 11th multiple of 3? ____   d What is the 50th multiple of 3? ____

e What is the 11th multiple of 4? ____   f What is the 50th multiple of 4? ____

g What is the 11th multiple of 5? ____   h What is the 50th multiple of 5? ____

Unit 4: Fractions

Remember

Fractions are part of a **whole**.

Two **halves** make a whole.

Three **thirds** make a whole.

Four **quarters** make a whole.

wholes

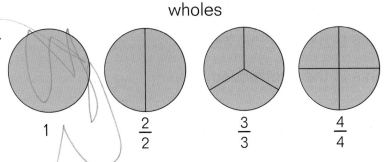

1      $\frac{2}{2}$ $\frac{3}{3}$ $\frac{4}{4}$

Have a go

1   Draw lines to show where you would cut each pizza.

a   Cut each pizza into halves.

There will be _____ slices altogether.

b   Cut each pizza into thirds.

There will be _____ slices altogether.

c   Cut each pizza into quarters.

There will be _____ slices altogether.

d   Cut each pizza into fifths.

There will be _____ slices altogether.

2   Show where you would cut in order to cut each biscuit into quarters.

  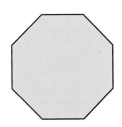 

Unit 5: Addition and subtraction facts

Remember

This is the addition sign: +

This is the subtraction sign: −

The order in which you add does not matter ➡ 4 + 12 equals 12 + 4

The order in which you subtract **does** matter ➡ 12 − 5 does not equal 5 − 12

Have a go

1 Complete these chains.

a 10 →(+4)○ →(−8)○ →(+5)○ →(+5)○ →(−2) 14

b 20 →(−3)○ →(−9)○ →(+4)○ →(+7)○ →(−7) 12

c 15 →(+3)○ →(−9)○ →(−4)○ →(+5)○ →(−10) 0

2 Write the missing + or − sign in each box.

a 9 ☐ 4 ☐ 2 = 11

b 8 ☐ 8 ☐ 2 = 2

c 7 ☐ 9 ☐ 3 = 13

d 5 ☐ 5 ☐ 4 = 6

e 6 ☐ 2 ☐ 9 = 13

f 8 ☐ 9 ☐ 3 = 14

3 Complete the table.

IN → + 9 − 3 → OUT

IN	4	6	7	9	12
OUT					

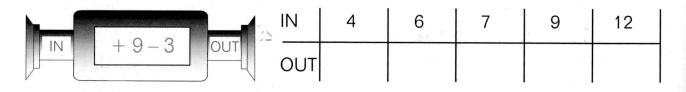

Unit 6: Addition

Remember

Sometimes, you have to **total** more than two numbers.

The total of 27, 45 and 74 is 27 + 45 + 74. The answer is 146.

Some additions you can work out in your head.
Others will require pencil and paper.
Always try to work out answers in your head first, as it will be quicker.

Have a go

1 Total these. Try to work some out in your head.

a

b
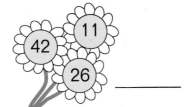

c

d

e

f
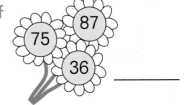

2 Answer the sums.

a
```
   35
   24
 + 35
 ____

 ____
```

b
```
   26
   38
 + 28
 ____

 ____
```

c
```
   19
   18
 + 27
 ____

 ____
```

d
```
   48
   19
 + 29
 ____

 ____
```

3 Work out the hidden digits.

a
```
   49
   15
 +  □9
 ____
   93
```

b
```
   27
   32
 + 1□
 ____
   77
```

c
```
   19
   29
 + 2□
 ____
   76
```

d
```
   43
   2□
 + 19
 ____
   90
```

11

Unit 7: Near differences

Remember

You can use **counting** to help you work out answers:
- When two numbers are close together, you can find the **difference** between them by counting on from the smaller number to the larger number.

The difference between 128 and 131 is **3**.

The difference between 299 and 305 is **6**.

- When the number you are adding or subtracting is small:

238 + 5 count on to get 243.

341 − 5 count back to get 336.

Have a go

1 Write down the differences between these pairs of numbers.

a   difference   b   difference

(128)(122) ➙ (   )   (168)(172) ➙ (   )

c   difference   d   difference

(299)(304) ➙ (   )   (632)(627) ➙ (   )

2 Add 4 to each number.

a   b

(99) ➙ (   )   (138) ➙ (   )

c   d

(287) ➙ (   )   (876) ➙ (   )

3 Subtract 6 from each number.

a   b

(105) ➙ (   )   (123) ➙ (   )

c   d

(402) ➙ (   )   (750) ➙ (   )

Remember

To find the difference between two numbers, count on from the smaller number.

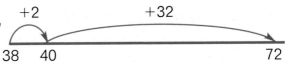

$+2$ $+32$

38   40   72

The difference between 72 and 38 is 34.

$32 + 2 = 34$

Always try to work out answers in your head first, as it will be quicker.

Have a go

1 Write the differences between these numbers.

a
| 27 | | 51 | ➔ | |

b
| 94 | | 28 | ➔ | |

c
| 81 | | 65 | ➔ | |

d
| 48 | | 73 | ➔ | |

e
| 33 | | 72 | ➔ | |

f
| 96 | | 48 | ➔ | |

2 Write the differences between the linked numbers.

a

| 63 | — | ▢ | — | 47 |

| ▢ | — | ▢ | — | ▢ |

| 28 | — | ▢ | — | 19 |

b

| 36 | — | ▢ | — | 84 |

| ▢ | — | ▢ | — | ▢ |

| 17 | — | ▢ | — | 36 |

Remember

You should be able to make numbers up to 100.
You can make 37 up to 100 in two jumps.

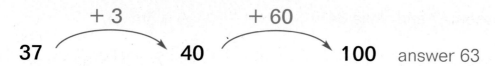

37    $+3$ 40 $+60$ 100   answer 63

Have a go

1   Make each number up to 100 in two jumps. Write what has been added.

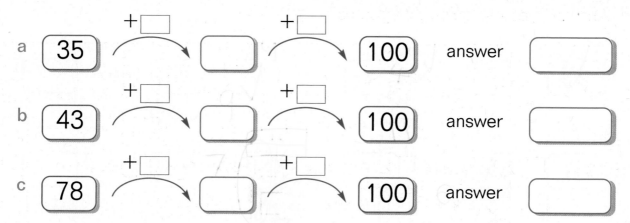

a   35 $+\square$ ⬜ $+\square$ 100   answer ⬜

b   43 $+\square$ ⬜ $+\square$ 100   answer ⬜

c   78 $+\square$ ⬜ $+\square$ 100   answer ⬜

2   Subtract each of these numbers from 100. Try to work the answers out in your head.

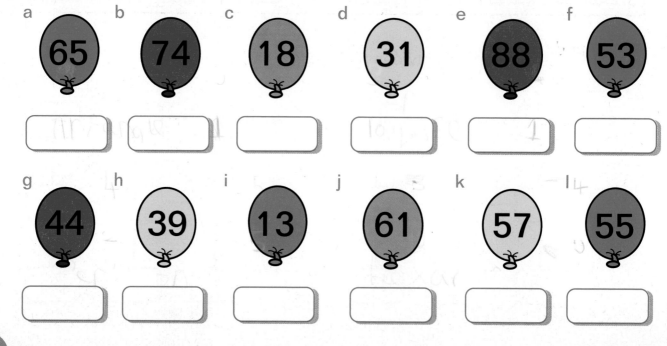

a   65   b   74   c   18   d   31   e   88   f   53

g   44   h   39   i   13   j   61   k   57   55

Unit 10: Multiplication facts

Remember

When learning your **tables**, you do not have as many facts to remember if you know this:

> **The order in which you multiply does not matter.**

3×4 has the same answer as 4×3 | 5×7 has the same answer as 7×5

$3 \times 4 = 12$ $4 \times 3 = 12$ | $5 \times 7 = 35$ $7 \times 5 = 35$

Have a go

1 Answer these as quickly as you can.

a	b	c	d	e
$2 \times 10 = 20$	$3 \times 7 = 21$	$2 \times 4 = \square$	$5 \times 5 = \square$	$10 \times 2 = \square$
$5 \times 7 = 35$	$7 \times 5 = 35$	$4 \times 7 = \square$	$7 \times 4 = \square$	$2 \times 6 = \square$
$3 \times 8 = 24$	$10 \times 8 = 80$	$5 \times 8 = \square$	$5 \times 10 = \square$	$8 \times 10 = \square$
$4 \times 2 = 8$	$6 \times 3 = 18$	$6 \times 4 = \square$	$3 \times 6 = \square$	$6 \times 10 = \square$
$3 \times 2 = 6$	$3 \times 3 = 9$	$10 \times 9 = \square$	$5 \times 9 = \square$	$8 \times 3 = \square$
$9 \times 5 = 45$	$9 \times 4 = \square$	$9 \times 2 = \square$	$3 \times 6 = \square$	$4 \times 4 = \square$

2 Write different multiplications for each number.

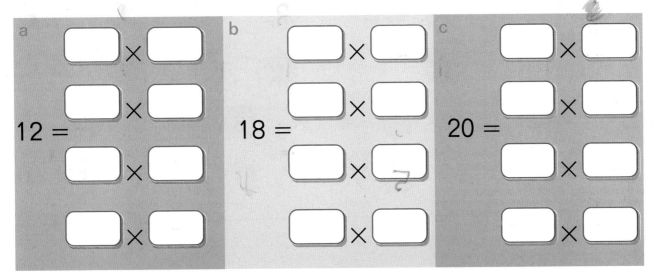

a   12 =

b   18 =

c   20 =

Unit 11: Division

Remember

Words like these are used when you divide:

> share   share equally   group   equal groups
> divide   division   divided by   divided into
> left   left over   remainder
> halve   half

Have a go

1 Answer these problems.

a What is 24 divided by 3? **8**

b What is 30 shared by 6? **5**

c What is 3 divided into 27? **9**

d What is 16 shared equally between 4? **4**

e What is a half of 18? **9**

f What is left when you divide 16 by 3? **11**

g What is 14 halved? **7** **9**

h What is the remainder if you divide 11 by 2? **6**

i How many 5s are in 35? **7**

j What is left over after dividing 34 by 5? **13**

2 What are the hidden numbers?

a **3** $\div 2 = 6$ b **5** $\div 3 = 7$ c **3** $\div 4 = 5$ d **2** $\div 3 = 6$

e $\div 5 = 6$ f **1** $\div 4 = 4$ g **10** $\div 2 = 5$ h **1** $\div 5 = 5$

i $16 \div$ **4** $= 4$ j $30 \div$ **5** $= 6$ k $24 \div$ **3** $= 8$ l $12 \div$ **4** $= 3$

m $14 \div$ **2** $= 7$ n $45 \div$ **5** $= 9$ o $70 \div$ **10** $= 7$ p $50 \div$ **5** $= 10$

Unit 12: Money

Remember

There are 100p in £1.
A **decimal point** is used to separate pounds from pennies.

£5.00 is the same as 500p or £5.
£1.75 is the same as 175p.
£3.05 is the same as 305p.
£0.25 is the same as 25p.

100p = £1.00

decimal point

Have a go

1 Write these pennies as pounds using a decimal point.

a 200p ➡ £ 2.00   b 400p ➡ £4.00   c 600p ➡ £ 6.00   d 800p ➡ £ 8.00

e 125p ➡ £ 1.25   f 368p ➡ £3.68   g 844p ➡ £8.44   h 501p ➡ £5.01

i 95p ➡ £95   j 30p ➡ £ 30   k 85p ➡ £85   l 10p ➡ £10

2 Write the totals in pounds using a decimal point.

a £1 35p → £1.35
b £2 65p → £2.65
c £5 7p → £5.7
d £5 50p → £5.50

e £1.20 £1.50 → £2.70
f £1.25 £1.15 → £2.40
g £1.40 £1.35 → £2.75
h £2.40 £3.30 → £5.70

i £2.40 £1.60 → £3
j £1.80 £1.40 → £3.20
k £2.50 £1.75 → £4.2
l 80p 90p → £1.80

3 Write the change from £5.

a 75p   Change £75

b 15p   Change £15

c £1.50   Change 60p

d £2.25   Change 45p

Remember

A right angle is a quarter of a turn.

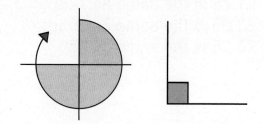

Four quarter turns make one full circle.

Here are the names of some 2D shapes with straight sides.

Triangle — three sides
Quadrilateral — four sides
Pentagon — five sides
Hexagon — six sides

Some 2D shapes have right angles.

Have a go

1 Tick each right angle.

a 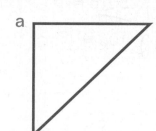 b 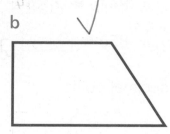 c 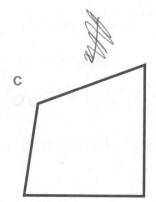 d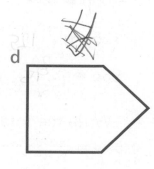

2 Write the name of each 2D shape.

a

triangle

b

Squre

c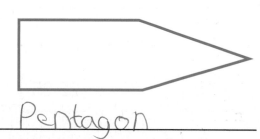

Pentagon

d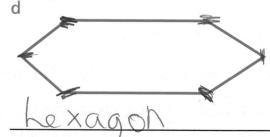

hexagon

Remember

Solid shapes have **faces**, **edges** and **corners**.

Another name for a corner is a **vertex**.

The name for more than one vertex is **vertices**.

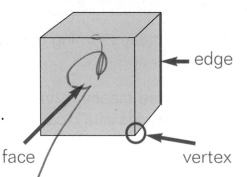

← edge

face   vertex

Have a go

1 Name each shape.

a

Cube

b

triangilar
prism

c

Cuboid

d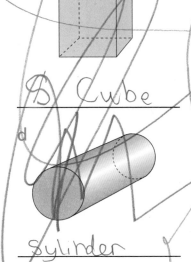

Sylinder

e

Spheaf

f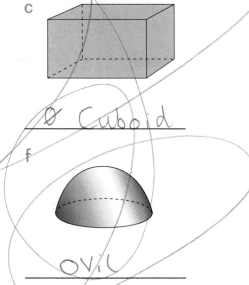

ovil

2 Look at the shapes above and answer the questions.

a Which shapes have no vertices? Sphere

b Which shape has only square faces? Cube

c Which shape has only one flat face? circle

d Which shape has exactly six vertices? hexagon

e Which shapes have rectangle faces? ob Sp Sphere

f Which shape has only two flat faces? hemasphere

Remember

Clockwise means turning the same way as the hands of a clock.

Anticlockwise means turning the opposite way to the hands of a clock.

clockwise   anticlockwise

Have a go

Write clockwise or anticlockwise to show the turn.

a

turn a tap on

_____

b

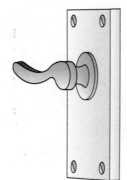

open this door

_____

c

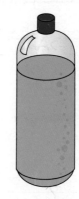

take off the cap

_____

d

turn the sound up

_____

e

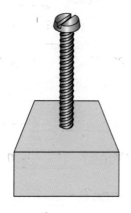

remove the screw

_____

f

tighten the nut

_____

Unit 16: Length

Remember

There are 100 **centimetres** in 1 metre. $100\,\text{cm} = 1\,\text{m}$
Some rulers have **millimetres** on them.

There are 10 **millimetres** in 1 **centimetre**. $10\,\text{mm} = 1\,\text{cm}$

Have a go

1 Measure each item to the nearest half centimetre.

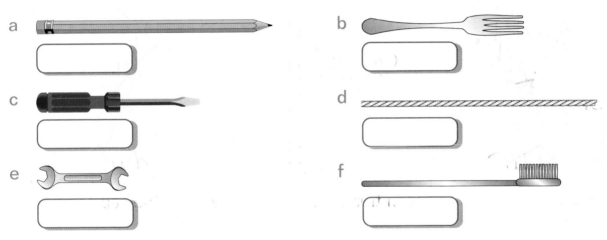

2 What must be added to make each of these up to 1 metre?

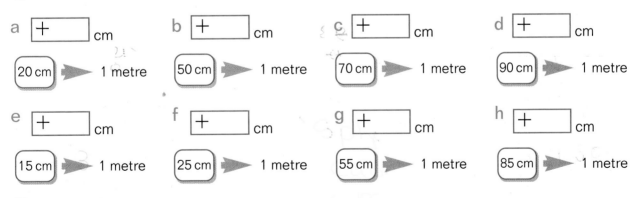

3 Answer these.

a How many cm in 2 metres? ▶ ☐

b How many cm in $\frac{1}{2}$ metre? ▶ ☐

c How many cm in $1\frac{1}{2}$ metres? ▶ ☐

Unit 17: Mass and capacity

Remember

When finding **mass**, you can use scales.
You have to work out what each mark on the scale is worth.

When finding **capacity**, you can use measuring jugs.
You have to work out what each mark on the jug is worth.

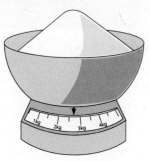

Each mark stands for $\frac{1}{2}$ kg.

Each mark stands for 100 ml.

Have a go

1. What is the reading on each of these scales?

   a

   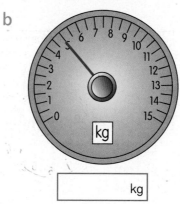

   _____ kg

   b

   _____ kg

   c

   _____ kg

2. Write how much liquid is in each measuring jug.

   a

   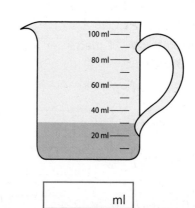

   _____ ml

   b

   _____ ml

   c

   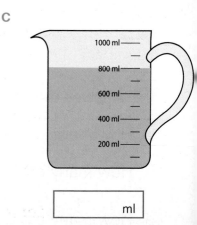

   _____ ml

Unit 18: Time

Remember

Sometimes we use the **quarters** when telling the time.

Have a go

1 Write these times using: quarter past, half past and quarter to.

a    b    c    d    e

_____ _____ _____ _____ _____

f    g    h    i    j

_____ _____ _____ _____ _____

2 Answer these questions about time.

a ☐ seconds = 1 minute   b ☐ minutes = 1 hour

c ☐ hours = 1 day   d ☐ days = 1 week

e ☐ days = 1 fortnight   f ☐ weeks = 1 year

g ☐ years = 1 decade   h ☐ years = 1 century

Unit 19: Graphs

Remember

Some **graphs** have **columns** or **bars** drawn on squares.

You must look carefully to see what each square is worth.

Sometimes, squares are worth 1, but sometimes they are worth more than 1.

Have a go

① Here is a graph showing some children's favourite crisps.

a How many children liked salt and vinegar crisps the best?

_____

b What was the most popular crisp? _____

c What was the least popular crisp? _____

d How many children were asked about their favourite crisp? _____

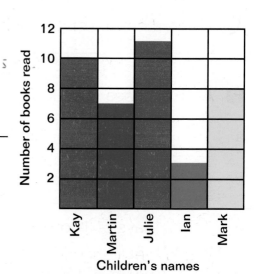

② Here is a graph showing the number of books read by some children.

a Who read the most books? _____

b Who read 7 books? _____

c How many books did Julie read? _____

d Who read more books than Mark? _____ and _____

e Who read fewer books than Martin? _____

f How many more books did Kay read than Ian? _____

Unit 20: Charts and tables

Remember

Sometimes you have to understand numbers that are in a **table**.
Tables have columns and rows.

column

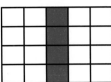
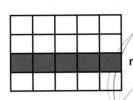

row

Have a go

1 Using the table on the right, answer these problems.

a How tall is the cow in centimetres?

_____

b Which animal stands about 50 cm high?

_____

c How many metres taller is the giraffe than
the camel? _____

d How many centimetres taller is the cow than
the dog? _____

e Which animal is nearest to your height?

_____

animal	height in metres
giraffe	6
elephant	$3\frac{1}{4}$
camel	2
cow	$1\frac{1}{2}$
dog	$\frac{1}{2}$

2 Using the table on the right, write the answers.

a Which job does Simon Denzil
have? _____

b Who is the vet? _____

c Who was born on 25.5.70?

_____

d Who is the oldest? _____

e Who is the youngest? _____

last name	first name	date of birth	job
Aziz	Abdul	25.5.70	teacher
Denzil	Simon	12.12.75	fitter
Earnshaw	Hannah	28.4.71	vet
Higham	Mandy	5.11.79	nurse
Lubna	Malik	9.1.69	doctor

Test 1

Check how much you have learned.

Answer the questions.
Mark your answers. Fill in your score.

SCORE

① Write the new number for each abacus.

a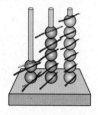

b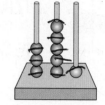

Add 4 [17]

Add 50 [59]

out of 2

②

a Make up to the next tens number.

643 ➔ 650

b Make up to the next hundreds number.

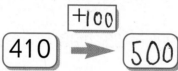

410 ➔ 500

out of 2

③ Measure the pencil to the nearest cm.

a 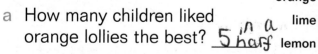 [~~X~~ 5 cm]

out of 2

b What must be added to the length of the pencil to make it 1 metre long? [95 cm]

④

favourite ice lollies

a How many children liked orange lollies the best? 5 *in a half*

b How many more liked strawberry than raspberry? 2

out of 2

⑤ Complete the table.

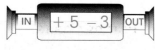

IN	6	8	10	12	14
OUT			12	15	20

out of 2

s to be cut

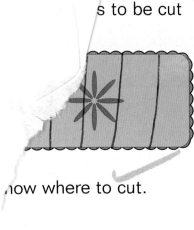

now where to cut.

3. b Name this shape.

hexxegen

8

a Draw hands to show the time.

Quarter to 4

b Write how many minutes.

Quarter of an hour = | 15 | minutes

9

a Total the numbers 36, 48 and 29. The total is _78_

b Work out the missing digit.

$$\begin{array}{r} 28 \\ 3\,\boxed{6} \\ +\ 17 \\ \hline 78 \end{array}$$

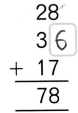

10 Work out the differences between the number pairs.

a | 34 | | 92 | difference ➡ | |

b | 71 | | 58 | difference ➡ | |

Test 2

Check how much you have learned.

Answer the questions.
Mark your answers. Fill in your score.

1 Answer these.

a What is the 20th multiple of 3? _____

b What is the 100th multiple of 5? _____

2

a What is the weight?   b What is the reading?

_____ kg   _____ ml

3 Write three different multiplications for the number 16.

$$16 = \boxed{} \times \boxed{}$$

4 Make 67 up to 100 in two jumps.

5 a Name each shape.

_____   _____   _____

b Which of the shapes has one circle face and one vertex?

_____

28

6 Tick the turn needed to turn the water off.

clockwise ☐

anticlockwise ☐

out of 1

7 Answer these.

a Write in figures:

two hundred and four _____

b Arrange these digits to make the largest even number.

| 3 | 5 | 0 | ___ ___ ___ |

out of 2

8 Answer these.

a What is 24 divided by 4? _____

b What is the remainder after dividing 15 by 4? _____

out of 2

9 Answer these.

a Write as pennies £3.70. _____

b Write as pounds 309p. _____

out of 2

10

	carrots	cucumber	tomatoes	apples	biscuits
Rabbit food					
Monday	2	1	2	1	5
Wednesday	3	1	2	2	4
Saturday	2	1	3	3	6

a How many biscuits were eaten altogether? _____

b On which day were three tomatoes eaten? _____

out of 2

Total out of 20

Parents' notes (Maths)

Unit 1: Place value   There are 10 digits: 0, 1, 2, 3, 4, 5, 6, 7, 8, and 9. The position of a digit in a number gives its value. For example, in 585 the digit 5 is worth 500 at the start of the number and only 5 at the end of the number. Ask your child to quickly add on 10 to a range of numbers that are larger than 100.

Unit 2: Reading and writing numbers   Your child should realise that numbers can be written in all sorts of ways – for example, using numbers, using words, using symbols, using dots or dashes. When you are out and about, set your child the challenge of finding numbers written in different ways.

Unit 3: Multiples   Your child needs to know that some, but not all, sequences go up in steps that are the same size. Your child needs to recognise patterns of 2s, 3s, 4s, 5s and 10s. These are called multiples. Multiples are answers to the multiplication tables, but they do not stop at the tenth fact – they go on and on. Ask your child for the hundredth multiple of many different numbers – the hundredth multiple of 4 is 400; the hundredth multiple of 5 is 500 and so on.

Unit 4: Fractions   Your child should know that when you divide a whole into fractions each part must be the same size. Talk about the difference between dividing something in two and dividing it in half. When you divide in two, the parts could be different sizes.

Unit 5: Addition and subtraction facts   Your child should know that an addition can be undone by a subtraction and a subtraction undone by an addition. For example, in □ + 9 = 17 the missing number can be found by subtracting 9 from 17: this undoes the addition by 9. Your child should also know the language of addition and subtraction, terms such as 'total', 'more than' and 'less than'.

Unit 6: Addition   Your child needs to be able to add together more than one pair of 2-digit numbers (numbers between 10 and 99). Sometimes, your child will need to use a pencil and paper, but at other times he or she should be able to work out the answer in his or her head. Explain that your child can add up the numbers in any order – the answer will still be the same.

Unit 7: Near differences   Your child should use counting skills when making a number up to the next ten or hundred. Check that he or she can make any tens or hundreds number up to the next ten by counting on in ones. Also, check that your child can make any tens number, such as 340, up to the next hundred by counting on in tens.

Unit 8: Counting on   One type of subtraction is called 'difference'. Difference is how many more one number is than another. You find the difference by subtracting the smaller number from the larger number.

Unit 9: Addition and subtraction   Two important mental mathematic skills are making numbers up to 100 and subtracting numbers from 100. As practice give your child a tens number and ask what must be added to make 100. When your child is confident with this, give him or her a fives number and ask what must be added to make 100.

Unit 10: Multiplication facts   By now, your child should have started to recall quickly the answers to tables facts for the 2, 3, 4, 5 and 10 times tables. Regular practice helps to sharpen up the recall of these facts. Explain that the order of the multiplication does not matter. So 3 × 4 gives the same answer as 4 × 3.

Unit 11: Division   Your child should know that the answer to a division can be checked by doing multiplication. So $12 \div 3 = 4$: CHECK $4 \times 3 = 12$. Your child should also know some of the words that we use to describe a division, such as halve, share, divide and group. As well as learning the tables facts for 2, 3, 4, 5 and 10, your child should know the corresponding division facts.

Unit 12: Money   Your child should know how to write down money using the decimal point to separate the pounds from the pennies, such as in £2.45. When you are out and about, encourage your child to look for labels written in pennies and those written in pounds and pennies.

Unit 13: 2D shapes   Your child needs to recognise common 2D shapes and right angles. Ask your child to find right angles in the room, using the corner of this book to check if he or she wishes.

Unit 14: 3D solids   Some 3D solids have faces, edges and corners (or vertices). Faces and edges can be flat or curved. Point out solids that your child can see in the room. *Which have flat faces? Which have curves? Which have vertices? Which have no vertices?*

Unit 15: Direction and movement   Your child should know that things can turn clockwise and anticlockwise. Talk about which way everyday items turn. Explain that some things may turn clockwise *and* anticlockwise – for example, it depends on which side of the door the handle is.

Unit 16: Length   Your child should know that there are 10 millimetres in 1 centimetre and 100 centimetres in 1 metre. Encourage your child to use a ruler or tape measure to find the lengths of several items in the room. He or she should measure some to the nearest centimetre and others to the nearest half centimetre.

Unit 17: Mass and capacity   Your child needs to be able to read scales when measuring mass and capacity, and to work out what each mark on the dial or scale stands for. Some children do not find this easy. Let your child use kitchen scales and measuring jugs to weigh objects and see how much things hold. *How heavy is this cup and how much does it hold?*

Unit 18: Time   As part of the work on time, your child needs to understand the terms 'quarter past', 'half past' and 'quarter to'. These terms are oral ways of saying the time, and your child is unlikely to see them written down. Eventually, your child should make the link between these times and 15 minutes past, 30 minutes past and 45 minutes past the hour.

Unit 19: Graphs   Your child needs to be able to read information from all sorts of tables, diagrams, charts and graphs. This unit expects your child to interpret bar and column graphs. A column graph always has vertical bars, while a bar graph can have horizontal or vertical bars. Talk about how the numbers go up in twos on the column graph.

Unit 20: Charts and tables   Your child will not always encounter calculations written down as numbers. Sometimes the mathematics is wrapped up in words or diagrams. Your child will have to choose what to do in order to solve the problem. Make sure that your child understands how a table of information works by talking about rows and columns.

Answers (Maths)

Unit 1: Place value (page 6)
a 430   b 870   c 740
d 508   e 903   f 206

Unit 2: Reading and writing numbers (page 7)
1. a 59   b 83   c 90
   d 500   e 106   f 360
   g 212   h 962

2. a 5   b 3   c 10
   d 12   e 7   f 9

3. a 3   b 9   c 3
   d 642   e 347

Unit 3: Multiples (page 8)
1. a 14 16 18 20 22 24 –
      multiples of 2
   b 18 21 24 27 30 33 –
      multiples of 3
   c 30 36 42 48 54 60 –
      multiples of 6

2. a 22   b 100   c 33   d 150
   e 44   f 200   g 55   h 250

Unit 4: Fractions (page 9)
1. a 6 slices

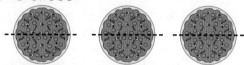

   b 6 slices

   c 8 slices

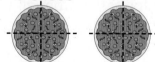

   d 15 slices

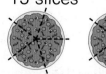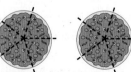

2. Check that the shapes are divided into four equal parts. These are some examples.

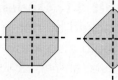

Unit 5: Addition and subtraction facts (page 10)
1. a 14   6   11   16
   b 17   8   12   19
   c 18   9   5   10

2. a $9 + 4 - 2 = 11$
   b $8 - 8 + 2 = 2$
   c $7 + 9 - 3 = 13$
   d $5 + 5 - 4 = 6$
   e $6 - 2 + 9 = 13$
   f $8 + 9 - 3 = 14$

3.
IN	4	6	7	9	12
OUT	10	12	13	15	18

Unit 6: Addition (page 11)
1. a 68   b 79   c 89
   d 123   e 173   f 198

2. a 94   b 92   c 64   d 96

3. a 2   b 8   c 8   d 8

Unit 7: Near differences (page 12)
1. a 6   b 4   c 5   d 5

2. a 103   b 142   c 291   d 880

3. a 99   b 117   c 396   d 744

Unit 8: Counting on (page 13)
1. a 24   b 66   c 16
   d 25   e 39   f 48

2. a

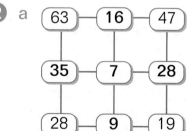

b (36)—(48)—(84)
(19)—(29)—(48)
(17)—(19)—(36)

Unit 9: Addition and subtraction (page 14)

1. a Check that numbers add up to 100 – answer 65
   b Check that numbers add up to 100 – answer 57
   c Check that numbers add up to 100 – answer 22

2. a 35   b 26   c 82
   d 69   e 12   f 47
   g 56   h 61   i 87
   j 39   k 43   l 45

Unit 10: Multiplication facts (page 15)

1. a 20 35 24 8   6   45
   b 21 35 80 18 9   36
   c 8   28 40 24 90 18
   d 25 28 50 18 45 18
   e 20 12 80 60 24 16

2. a Answers could be:
   2 × 6   6 × 2   3 × 4   4 × 3
   1 × 12   12 × 1
   b Answers could be:
   2 × 9   9 × 2   3 × 6   6 × 3
   1 × 18   18 × 1
   c Answers could be:
   2 × 10   10 × 2   4 × 5   5 × 4
   1 × 20   20 × 1

Unit 11: Division (page 16)

1. a 8   b 5   c 9
   d 4   e 9   f 1
   g 7   h 1   i 7
   j 4

2. a 12   b 21   c 20   d 18
   e 30   f 16   g 10   h 25
   i 4   j 5   k 3   l 4
   m 2   n 5   o 10   p 5

Unit 12: Money (page 17)

1. a £2.00   b £4.00   c £6.00
   d £8.00   e £1.25   f £3.68
   g £8.44   h £5.01   i £0.95
   j £0.30   k £0.85   l £0.10

2. a £1.35   b £2.65   c £5.07
   d £5.50   e £2.70   f £2.40
   g £2.75   h £5.70   i £4.00
   j £3.20   k £4.25   l £1.70

3. a £4.25   b £4.85   c £3.50
   d £2.75

Unit 13: 2D shapes (page 18)

2. a triangle   b quadrilateral
   c pentagon   d hexagon

Unit 14: 3D solids (page 19)

1. a cube   b triangular prism
   c cuboid   d cylinder
   e sphere   f hemisphere

2. a cylinder, sphere, hemisphere
   b cube   c hemisphere
   d triangular prism
   e triangular prism and cuboid
   f cylinder

Unit 15: Direction and movement (page 20)

a anticlockwise   b anticlockwise
c anticlockwise   d clockwise
e anticlockwise   f clockwise

Unit 16: Length (page 21)

1. a $6\frac{1}{2}$ cm   b $4\frac{1}{2}$ cm

c $4\frac{1}{2}$ cm   d $6\frac{1}{2}$ cm

e $2\frac{1}{2}$ cm   f $5\frac{1}{2}$ cm

2 a 80 cm   b 50 cm   c 30 cm
   d 10 cm   e 85 cm   f 75 cm
   g 45 cm   h 15 cm

3 a 200 cm   b 50 cm   c 150 cm

Unit 17: Mass and capacity (page 22)
1 a 7 kg   b 5 kg   c 11 kg

2 a 60 ml   b 30 ml   c 800 ml

Unit 18: Time (page 23)
1 a quarter past 2   b half past 10
   c half past 7   d quarter to 5
   e quarter past 12 f quarter past 11
   g quarter to 6   h quarter past 6
   i half past 2   j quarter to 5

2 a 60 secs   b 60 mins c 24 hours
   d 7 days   e 14 days f 52 weeks
   g 10 years h 100 years

Unit 19: Graphs (page 24)
1 a 4 b plain c pickled onion d 20

2 a Julie   b Martin c 11
   d Kay and Julie e Ian   f 7

Unit 20: Charts and tables (page 25)
1 a 150 cm   b dog
   c 4 m   d 100 cm
   e Check that a sensible answer
     is given.

2 a fitter
   b Hannah Earnshaw
   c Abdul Aziz
   d Malik Lubna
   e Mandy Higham

Test 1 (pages 26 and 27)
1 a 260   b 401

2 a + 7 = 650   b + 90 = 500

3 a 5 cm   b 95 cm

4 a 11   b 4

5

IN	6	8	10	13	18
OUT	8	10	12	15	20

6 a 20 slices
   b

7 a   ✓   b hexagon

   ✓

8 a   b 15 minutes

9 a 113   b 3

10 a 58   b 13

Test 2 (pages 28 and 29)
1 a 60   b 500

2 a 9 kg   b 50 ml

3 2 × 8   1 × 16   4 × 4
   8 × 2   16 × 1 (any three)

4 33 (make sure the numbers add
   up to 100)

5 a cylinder   sphere   cone
   b cone

6 clockwise

7 a 204   b 530

8 a 6   b 3

9 a 370p   b £3.09

10 a 15   b Saturday

Unit 1: Using exclamation marks

Remember

An **exclamation** always **begins** with a **capital letter** and **ends** with an **exclamation mark**. We use exclamation marks to show we **feel strongly** about something.

Don't push me!

This exclamation shows strong feelings.

What a lovely present!

This exclamation shows surprise.

Have a go

1 Rewrite each exclamation correctly.

a come here at once _____

b stop pinching me _____

c don't do that _____

d what a lovely picture _____

e it's not fair _____

f this is terrible _____

g how sensible you are _____

h be quiet _____

2 Write an exclamation you might make if . . .

a

. . . you met a monster.

b

. . . you won the Lottery.

c

. . . your best trainers got muddy.

d

. . . you saw a thief snatching a woman's bag.

e

. . . someone was bullying you.

f

. . . you got a lovely birthday present.

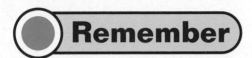

Remember

A **phoneme** is the **smallest unit of sound** in a word. A phoneme may be made up of **one or more letters** which make **one sound**.

b + oa + t = boat
(3 phonemes)

Have a go

Think of, and write down, two words containing each of the following phonemes:

a	**ir** (as in g**ir**l)	
b	**oy** (as in b**oy**)	
c	**ou** (as in l**ou**d)	
d	**aw** (as in p**aw**)	
e	**y** (as in m**y**)	
f	**or** (as in t**or**n)	
g	**oi** (as in b**oi**l)	
h	**ow** (as in c**ow**)	

Unit 3: Collective nouns

Remember

A **collective noun** is the name given to a **group** of things.

a **bunch** of flowers

a **flock** of sheep

Have a go

1 Choose the correct noun to complete each phrase.

| pack | gaggle | gang | bunch | herd | fleet | team | shoal |

a a _____ of bananas

b a _____ of thieves

c a _____ of geese

d a _____ of cows

e a _____ of fish

f a _____ of cards

g a _____ of ships

h a _____ of footballers

2 Complete each sentence with a suitable collective noun.

a Tom gave his mum a _____ of flowers.

b The woman was proud of her _____ of stamps.

c The girl was chased by an angry _____ of wasps.

d The bird laid a _____ of eggs.

e The _____ of wolves lived in the forest.

f The _____ of spectators roared.

g The _____ of birds flew into the sky.

Unit 4: The use of commas

Remember

Commas help to **break up** long sentences into **smaller parts**.

Sam's car, a blue sports car, was brand new.

Have a go

1 Put in the missing commas.

a Julie jumped in the puddle a large muddy puddle on her way to school.

b The giant a huge man wore a big pairs of boots.

c The car an old rusty banger parked near our house.

d John the shorter of the twins smiled sweetly.

e The bird a fat wood pigeon had a drink from the pond.

f The thief who had just escaped from jail was soon captured by the police.

g I saw two people an old woman and a small boy in the library.

h Some people very brave people are not afraid of ghosts.

2 Think of a suitable ending for each sentence.

a To my surprise, _____ .

b After the storm, _____ .

c All of a sudden, _____ .

d Although I was thirsty, _____ .

e During the night, _____ .

f As soon as the snow stopped, _____ .

g On the seabed, _____ .

Unit 5: Letter patterns – *ore*

Remember

Always look carefully at words to see if
you can spot any **common letter patterns**.

I ad**ore** the seash**ore**.

Have a go

1 Make these words. Read the words you make.

ore

b**ore**_____   c_____   m_____   s_____   t_____   w_____

bore_____   _____   _____   _____   _____   _____

ore

ad_____   st_____   sn_____   sc_____   sw_____   bef_____

_____   _____   _____   _____   _____   _____

2 Write the **ore** word that means:

a _____   to make a loud noise while asleep

b _____   to love

c _____   painful when it is touched

d _____   the middle of an apple

e _____   come in front of

f _____   to keep things until they are needed

g _____   to get a goal or a point in a game

h _____   to make a hole with a drill

i _____   a larger number or amount

j _____   said a rude word

Remember

Compound words are made up of **two smaller words joined together**.

cup + board = cupboard

Have a go

Make some compound words.

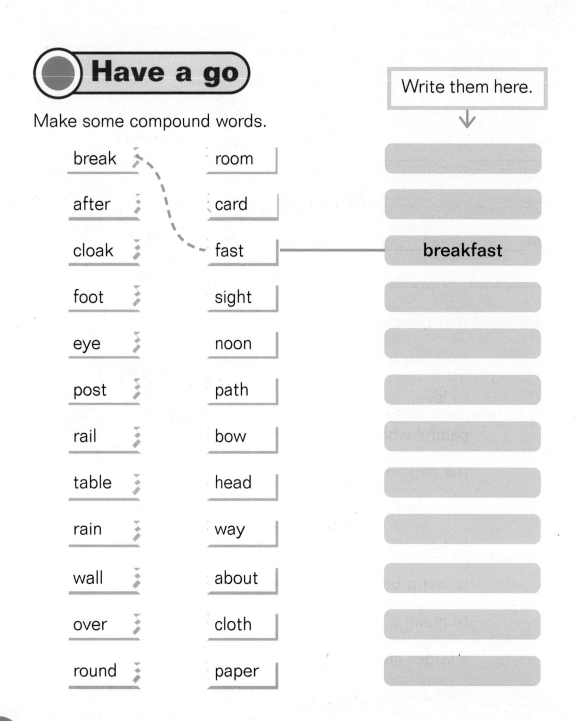

Write them here.

break	room
after	card
cloak	fast
foot	sight
eye	noon
post	path
rail	bow
table	head
rain	way
wall	about
over	cloth
round	paper

breakfast

Unit 7: Revising verb tenses

Remember

When we are writing about something that happened **in the past**, we use the **past tense** of verbs.

| Today I **am swimming** in the river. This is happening **now**, so the verb is in the **present tense**. | Yesterday I **swam** in the sea. This happened in the **past**, so the verb is in the **past tense**. |

 Have a go

1 Match the present tense of each verb with its correct past tense.

present tense	past tense	present tense	past tense
I see.	I rode.	I catch.	I was.
I go.	I broke.	I am.	I flew.
I ride.	I saw.	I write.	I fell.
I make.	I ate.	I fly.	I caught.
I break.	I went.	I ring.	I wrote.
I eat.	I made.	I fall.	I rang.

2 Choose the correct form of the verb to complete each sentence.

a Last night I (goed, went) _____ to a party.

b When I washed up I (breaked, broke) _____ a plate.

c We (rided, rode) _____ our bikes in the rain.

d The girl (beginned, began) _____ to shout.

e The man (buyed, bought) _____ some potatoes.

f I (ringed, rang) _____ the doorbell.

g I soon (eated, ate) _____ my sandwiches.

h We all (seed, saw) _____ the accident.

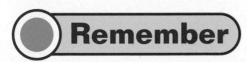

Remember

A dictionary may be used to help you check the **spelling** of words.

choclate ☒   choclet ☒   chocolet ☒   chocolate ☑

Have a go

Each of the 20 words in this spelling test is spelt incorrectly.
Look them up in a dictionary and write each word correctly.

a yung _____   b biscit _____

c frend _____   d ushual _____

e becos _____   f horribal _____

g harf _____   h gess _____

i diffrent _____   j advencher _____

k suddenley _____   l anser _____

m somthing _____   n qwiet _____

o enywhere _____   p enormus _____

q Wensday _____   r autum _____

s intresting _____   t noisey _____

Unit 9: Revising rhyming

Remember

We must **listen** carefully to identify words that **rhyme**.
Some **rhyming words** sound alike but do not contain the **same letter patterns**.

I **thought** you liked **sport!**

Have a go

Match up the pairs of rhyming words.

Write them here.

boil	pair
blood	dried
scare	royal
sound	daughter
sky	mud
tide	weight
water	drowned
past	paws
late	high
cause	passed
through	bird
heard	true

boil   royal

Remember

A **prefix** is a **group of letters** we add on to the **front** of a word.
Prefixes change the **meaning** of the word.

mis + behave = **mis**behave   ex + clude = **ex**clude
mis means 'wrongly' or 'badly'   **ex** means 'out of' or 'away from'

Have a go

1 Make the words. Read the words you make.

a

| | behave → | **misbehave** | b | | hausted → | _____ |

mis → spell → _____   ex → pand → _____

mis → judge → _____   ex → clude → _____

calculate → _____   port → _____

handle → _____   it → _____

2 Write the word that means:

a _____ to calculate wrongly

b _____ to get bigger

c _____ tired out

d _____ to behave badly

e _____ to handle badly

f _____ to leave out

g _____ to judge something wrongly

h _____ the way out of a place

i _____ goods that are sent out of the country

j _____ to make a spelling mistake

Unit 11: Revising adjectives

Remember

An adjective is a **describing** word.
An adjective gives us more **information about a noun**.

a fluffy rabbit

Have a go

1 Match up the pairs of adjectives that mean the same.

Write them here.

big	scared
nice	horrible
nasty	broad
frightened	large
sly	dear
wide	tiny
expensive	pleasant
small	cunning

_____

_____

_____

_____ big   large _____

_____

_____

_____

_____

2 Write an adjective that means the opposite to each of these:

a new _____

b shallow _____

c quiet _____

d rough _____

e fast _____

f tall _____

g interesting _____

h rude _____

i empty _____

j near _____

k cold _____

l thin _____

Remember

Some words contain **silent letters**.
We cannot hear them when we say the words.

talk   listen

Have a go

1 Make the words. Read the words you make.

t

a   lis **t** en   rus__le   glis__en   bus__le
     __listen__   _____   _____   _____

| l |

b   ta__k   pa__m   ha__f   ca__m   cha__k   ca__f
     ____   ____   ____   ____   ____   ____

2 Write the word from question 1 that rhymes with:

a talk _____   b listen _____   c palm _____

d rustle _____   e half _____

3 Use the words to complete these sentences.

a You use _____ to write on a blackboard.

b Your _____ is part of your hand.

c I cut the apple in _____ .

d It is rude to _____ with your mouth full.

e You should _____ carefully to good advice.

f The wind made the leaves _____ .

g A _____ is a baby cow.

h To _____ means to hurry about in a busy way.

i Snow will _____ in the light.

j Try to stay _____ when you feel angry.

 Remember

A **suffix** is a **group of letters** we add to the **end** of a word.
A suffix changes the **meaning** of the word.
We can change some **nouns** into **adjectives** by adding the suffix **y**.

smell + y = smelly
(noun)   (adjective)

noise + y = noisy
(noun)   (adjective)

sun + y = sunny
(noun)   (adjective)

We just add **y** to some words.

If the word ends in **e**, we **drop the e** and add **y**.

We have to **double** the **last letter** of some words before we add **y**.

 Have a go

Change each noun into an adjective by adding the suffix **y**.

Set A

a oil _____   b dust _____   c cloud _____

d rain _____   e curl _____   f greed _____

Set B

a noise _____   b shade _____   c stripe _____

d ease _____   e stone _____   f slime _____

Set C

a mud _____   b nut _____   c fat _____

d jam _____   e bag _____   f sun _____

Set D

a twist _____   b ice _____   c crisp _____

d fog _____   e fun _____   f water _____

g rust _____   h scare _____   i rat _____

j grime _____   k spot _____   l fault _____

Unit 14: Revising apostrophes

Remember

We can **shorten** some words by missing some letters out.
We put an **apostrophe** to show where letters are missing.

Who's that player?

who's = who is

I've no idea.

I've = I have

Have a go

Write each sentence again. Write the shorter form of the underlined words.

a <u>I have</u> got a new video game.
   I've got a new video game.

b The weather <u>was not</u> very nice.

_____

c It <u>would not</u> be nice to get all my spellings wrong.

_____

d <u>We are</u> all going on our summer holiday.

_____

e <u>She will</u> get lost if <u>she is</u> not careful.

_____

f The children <u>are not</u> looking where <u>they are</u> going.

_____

g You <u>must not</u> run across a busy road.

_____

h I <u>could not</u> find my keys which <u>I had</u> hidden.

_____

i <u>Where is</u> the buried treasure?

_____

j <u>We have</u> got to go now or <u>we will</u> be late.

_____

Unit 15: Revising singular and plural

Remember

Singular means one. Plural means more than one.

loaf   loaves   potatoes   tomatoes

If a noun ends with **f** (or **fe**), we change the **f** to **v** and add **es** to make it plural.

If a noun ends with **o**, we often add **es** to make it plural.

Have a go

1 Write the plural of:

a half _____

b potato _____

c shelf _____

d hero _____

e loaf _____

f thief _____

g tomato _____

h knife _____

i leaf _____

j volcano _____

k calf _____

l echo _____

2 Fill in the plural form of each noun in the gaps.

a Some _____ (wolf) live in the woods.

b Lots of _____ (leaf) fell from the trees.

c I put two _____ (loaf) into my trolley.

d The farmer lifted the sack of _____ (potato) off the tractor.

e Two _____ (thief) stole some jewels from the shop.

f Several _____ (hero) returned from the war.

g I returned the books to the _____ (shelf) in the library.

h Do you like green _____ (tomato)?

i I cut the cake into two equal _____ (half).

j Both _____ (volcano) were erupting.

Unit 16: Using personal pronouns

Remember

A **pronoun** is a word that **takes the place of a noun**.
A **personal pronoun** takes the place of the **name of a person**.

Sarah stopped when **she** (Sarah) came to the traffic lights.

Have a go

1 Find and circle ten personal pronouns, reading across.

a	b	m e	c	d	t	h	e	m
m	h	u	s	j	k	l	y	o	u
h	i	m	z	x	c	s	h	e	k
b	v	c	h	e	p	d	i	t	a
p	t	h	e	y	q	w	e	z	x

2 Write who or what each underlined pronoun stands for.

a   The boy ran after the ball and kicked <u>it</u> (<u>the ball</u>).

b   Emma had a dog. <u>She</u> (_____) took <u>it</u> (_____) everywhere.

c   "<u>I</u> (_____) like football," Joe said.

d   "Come with <u>us</u> (_____)," Amy and Grace said.

e   The man wanted the car but <u>it</u> (_____) was too dear for <u>him</u> (_____).

f   The children played with the toys but <u>they</u> (_____) were broken.

g   "Are <u>you</u> (_____) ready?" Mrs Jones asked Tara and Anna.

h   When the dog saw the burglar, <u>it</u> (_____) chased <u>him</u> (_____).

Unit 17: Subject and verb agreement

Remember

Every sentence must have a **verb**.
Every verb must have a **subject** (the person or thing that goes with the verb).
The subject and verb must always **agree**.

The lights shines brightly. ✗   The lights shine brightly. ✓

Have a go

1 Use **is** or **are** to complete each sentence.

a It _____ a lovely day.

b They _____ singing.

c He _____ asleep.

d We _____ going out.

e She _____ going home.

f You _____ not right.

g _____ it too hot?

h _____ they working hard?

2 Correct the underlined verb in each sentence.

a A panda ~~have~~ a round face with small ears. __has__

b Pandas <u>spends</u> ten hours a day asleep. _____

c The cat and the dog <u>was</u> great friends. _____

d Each of the girls <u>have</u> a toy. _____

e Every child <u>are</u> ready. _____

f Neither of the children <u>were</u> singing. _____

g Everybody <u>were</u> delighted. _____

h None of the ships <u>were</u> sunk. _____

i <u>Are</u> your friend coming? _____

j Not one of the children <u>have</u> a pencil. _____

Unit 18: Revising conjunctions

Remember

A **conjunction** is a **joining** word. We use a **conjunction** to join two short sentences together to make one longer sentence.

The moon came out. The clock struck midnight.
The moon came out **as** the clock struck midnight.

Have a go

1 Choose the best conjunction to join each pair of sentences.

a It was difficult to see _____ it was so dark. (so, because)

b You will hurt yourself _____ you fall off your bike. (if, and)

c I drank a lot of water _____ I was thirsty. (if, because)

d My brother was pleased _____ I gave him a present. (but, when)

e It was freezing _____ I put on my coat. (because, so)

f The door has been broken _____ I slammed it. (since, although)

g I looked at the clock _____ it had stopped. (and, but)

h I did my homework early _____ I could watch television. (so, and)

2 Think of a good ending for each sentence. Underline the conjunction in each.

a Sam, was breathless because _____

b The toy had been broken since _____

c I was sad when _____

d We went for a walk although _____

e He would not have scored the goal if _____

f It was raining so _____

g We went to the circus where _____

Remember

Synonyms are words that have **similar meanings**.

The car **sped** past.

The car **zoomed** past.

Have a go

1 Underline the pair of verbs in each set which have similar meaning.

a smile grin frown

b crash smash hide

c speak hop talk

d pull eat drag

e draw cut slit

f cook bake lift

g pop listen hear

h tap watch look

2 Write the verbs from the box in the correct columns of the chart, under the verbs with similar meanings.

| squeeze | glow | hold | bang | crush |
| consume | hit | sparkle | grab | swallow |

squash	eat	shine	grip	knock

Unit 20: Revising speech marks

Remember

The words people actually say go inside **speech marks**.
You should never **close** speech marks without putting in a **punctuation mark**.

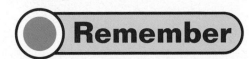

Have you seen my socks anywhere?

Jack said, "Have you seen my socks anywhere?"

Have a go

Rewrite these sentences and punctuate them correctly.

a   the teacher asked, why are you late

   <u>The teacher asked, "Why are you late?"</u>

b   emma said, my pet rabbit has escaped

   _____

c   mr dean shouted, keep off my garden

   _____

d   mrs james said, it is time to go home

   _____

e   tom said, can you help me do my jigsaw

   _____

f   sharon said, bananas are my favourite fruit

   _____

g   the driver asked, how far is it to London

   _____

h   the pirate shouted, tell me where you have hidden the gold

   _____

i   uncle john exclaimed, what a lovely surprise

   _____

j   the doctor asked, what is the matter

   _____

Test 1

Check how much you have learned.

Answer the questions.
Mark your answers. Fill in your score.

1 Write these exclamations correctly.

a (stop shouting)   b (how lovely)

_____   _____

out of 2

2 Fill in the missing phoneme in each word.

a

p___se

b

cl___d

out of 2

3 Choose the best word to fill each gap.

a   a _____ (packet, bunch) of bananas

b   a _____ (pile, flock) of stones

out of 2

4 Fill in the missing commas in the sentences.

a The bird a yellow budgie flapped its wings.

b Both jumpers the green and the blue one were mine.

out of 2

5 Choose the correct word to complete each sentence.

a Some people _____ (snore, store) in bed.

b I put the apple _____ (sore, core) in the bin.

out of 2

6 The two compound words have got mixed up. Write them correctly.

a

cupbow

_____

b

rainboard

_____

7 Choose the correct word to complete each sentence.

a Have you ever _____ (seed, seen) a ghost?

b The boy _____ (catched, caught) a cold.

out of 2

8 Spell these words correctly. Use a dictionary to help you.

a becos _____   b terribal _____

out of 2

9 Underline the pair of rhyming words in each set.

a   **bird   sort   hurt   taught**

b   **leap   boot   home   roam**

out of 2

10 Choose **mis** or **ex** to begin each word.

a _____ port

b _____ judge

out of 2

Total out of 20

Test 2

Check how much you have learned.

Answer the questions.
Mark your answers. Fill in your score.

1 Write an adjective that means the opposite of:

a dark _____

b expensive _____

out of 2

2 Choose **l** or **t** to complete each word.

a

lis__en

b

ta__k

out of 2

3 Spell these words correctly:

a

stoney _____

b

spoty _____

out of 2

4 Write the longer form of the underlined words.

a <u>We're</u> going shopping.

_____ _____ going shopping.

b I <u>couldn't</u> do it.

I _____ _____ do it.

out of 2

5 Fill in the missing plurals.

a one leaf   lots of _____

b one potato   a sack of _____

out of 2

6 Write who or what each underlined pronoun stands for.

a Amy loves to read when <u>she</u> (_____) is in bed.

b The dog got muddy when <u>it</u> (_____) rolled in a puddle.

7 Choose the correct verb to fill each gap.

a Each of the apples _____ (is, are) green.

b None of the bananas _____ (was, were) ripe.

8 Choose the best conjunction for each gap.

a You will cry _____ (if, so) you bang your thumb.

b I picked up the phone _____ (when, but) it rang.

9 Underline the pair of synonyms in each set.

a | cry | eat | sob | lift |

b | eat | run | race | sleep |

10 Rewrite the sentences and punctuate them correctly.

a the teacher said, get our your books

_____

b the child asked, is it time to go home

_____

Parents' notes (English)

Unit 1: Using exclamation marks   Remind your child that an exclamation always begins with a capital letter and ends with an exclamation mark. We use exclamations when we feel strongly about something.

Unit 2: Revising phonemes   All words are made up of phonemes (units of sound). Sometimes phonemes may be single letters. Sometimes they consist of two or more letters which make one sound e.g. **ou** and **ow**. Your child needs to know how to build up words using phonemes.

Unit 3: Collective nouns   Collective nouns are the names given to groups of things e.g. flock of sheep.

Unit 4: The use of commas   Remind your child that we sometimes use commas to break up long sentences into smaller parts to help them make more sense.

Unit 5: Letter patterns – *ore*   There are many common letter patterns (letters which frequently come together) in words. It is important for your child to recognise these when reading and to be able to use them when writing. The letter pattern **ore** is the focus of this unit.

Unit 6: Compound words   Compound words are words that are made by joining two smaller words together to make one longer word.

Unit 7: Revising verb tenses   Remind your child that when a verb tells of an action taking place now, we say that it is written in the present tense. When the verb tells of an action that has already taken place it is written in the past tense.

Unit 8: Using a dictionary   A dictionary is a very valuable tool. Your child needs to know how to use one. This unit focuses on using a dictionary as an aid to spelling.

Unit 9: Revising rhyming   Rhyming involves good listening skills. The ability to differentiate and hear differences in sounds and rhymes is an important early reading and spelling skill. In this unit, the rhyming part of the pairs of words sound similar but are spelt differently.

Unit 10: Prefixes – *mis* and *ex*   A prefix is a group of letters we can add to the front of a word. Prefixes change the meaning of the word. In this unit the prefixes 'mis' (meaning 'wrongly' or 'badly') and 'ex' (meaning 'out of' or 'away from') are featured.

Unit 11: Revising adjectives   An adjective is a describing word. It tells us more about a noun. Adjectives help us make our writing more interesting and descriptive.

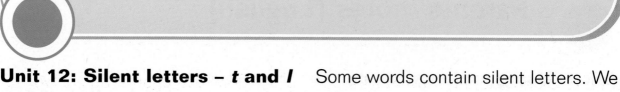

Unit 12: Silent letters – *t* and *l*   Some words contain silent letters. We can't hear these when we say the words. Note how the silent letters **t** and **l** come within each word.

Unit 13: Suffixes – *y*   A suffix is a group of letters we add to the end of a word. Your child needs to understand that many words may be extended by adding suffixes. Adding a suffix changes the meaning of the word in some way. In this unit it is shown how nouns may be changed into adjectives by the addition of the suffix **y**.

Unit 14: Revising apostrophes   We sometimes shorten words and miss out letters. These words are called contractions. (To 'contract' means to make shorter.) We use an apostrophe to show where letters are missing. We use contractions a lot in spoken language but less so in written language.

Unit 15: Revising singular and plural   Nouns may be singular (when there is only one) or plural (when there is more than one). The most common way to make a noun plural is to add **s** (as in 'trees'). However, sometimes the spelling of the plural noun is made in other ways (as in the examples in this unit).

Unit 16: Using personal pronouns   A pronoun is a word that takes the place of a noun. ('Pro' actually means 'in place of'.) We use pronouns to avoid a lot of repetition in sentences.

Unit 17: Subject and verb agreement   When children are writing, very often their minds go faster than their pens. One common mistake is for the verb in the sentence not to agree with the subject (the main thing or person) in the sentence.

Unit 18: Revising conjunctions   A conjunction is a joining word which may be used to join two sentences together. (Encourage your child to remember this by likening it to a road junction, where two roads join together.)

Unit 19: Revising synonyms   Synonyms are words which have the same, or very similar meanings. Using synonyms makes our writing more interesting and adds variety. Encourage your child to use a thesaurus if you have one.

Unit 20: Revising speech marks   When we write down what people say, we use speech marks. Remind your child that the words a person says should go inside the speech marks.

Answers (English)

Unit 1: Using exclamation marks (page 35)

1
a Come here at once!
b Stop pinching me!
c Don't do that!
d What a lovely picture!
e It's not fair!
f This is terrible!
g How sensible you are!
h Be quiet!

2 Children's own answers. Ensure each exclamation ends with an exclamation mark.

Unit 2: Revising phonemes (page 36)
There are other possible answers.
a swirl, twirl
b toy, coy
c proud, cloud
d saw, straw
e try, sty
f thorn, born
g spoil, toil
h how, bow

Unit 3: Collective nouns (page 37)

1
a bunch
b gang
c gaggle
d herd
e shoal
f pack
g fleet
h team

2
a bunch
b collection
c swarm
d clutch
e pack
f crowd
g flock

Unit 4: The use of commas (page 38)

1
a Julie jumped in the puddle, a large muddy puddle, on her way to school.
b The giant, a huge man, wore a big pair of boots.
c The car, an old rusty banger, parked near our house.
d John, the shorter of the twins, smiled sweetly.
e The bird, a fat wood pigeon, had a drink from the pond.
f The thief, who had just escaped from jail, was soon captured by the police.
g I saw two people, an old woman and a small boy, in the library.
h Some people, very brave people, are not afraid of ghosts.

2 Check that each sentence ending is suitable, correctly spelt and punctuated.

Unit 5: Letter patterns – *ore* (page 39)

1 bore, core, more sore, tore, wore, adore, store, snore, score, swore, before

2
a snore
b adore
c sore
d core
e before
f store
g score
h bore
i more
j swore

Unit 6: Compound words (page 40)

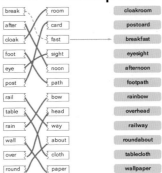

Unit 7: Revising verb tenses (page 41)

2
a went
b broke
c rode
d began
e bought
f rang
g ate
h saw

Unit 8: Using a dictionary (page 42)
a young
b biscuit
c friend
d usual
e because
f horrible
g half
h guess
i different

j adventure k suddenly l answer
m something n quiet o anywhere
p enormous q Wednesday r autumn
s interesting y noisy

Unit 9: Revising rhyming (page 43)

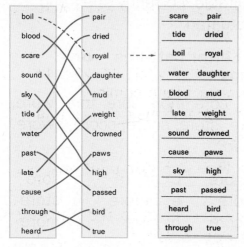

Unit 10: Prefixes – *mis* and *ex* (page 44)

1 a misbehave misspell misjudge
miscalculate mishandle

b exhausted expand exclude
export exit

2 a miscalculate b expand
c exhausted d misbehave
e mishandle f exclude
g misjudge h exit
i export j misspell

Unit 11: Revising adjectives (page 45)

1

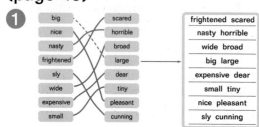

2 a old b deep c loud
d smooth e slow f short
g boring h polite i full
j far k hot l fat

Unit 12: Silent letters – *t* and *l* (page 46)

1 a listen rustle glisten bustle
b talk palm half calm
chalk calf

2 a chalk b glisten c calm
d bustle e calf

3 a chalk b palm c half
d talk e listen f rustle
g calf h bustle i glisten
j calm

Unit 13: Suffixes – *y* (page 47)

Set A: a oily b dusty c cloudy
d rainy e curly f greedy
Set B: a noisy b shady c stripy
d easy e stony f slimy
Set C: a muddy b nutty c fatty
d jammy e baggy f sunny
Set D: a twisty b icy c crispy
d foggy e funny f watery
g rusty h scary i ratty
j grimy k spotty l faulty

Unit 14: Revising apostrophes (page 48)

a I've got a new video game.
b The weather wasn't very nice.
c It wouldn't be nice to get all my
spellings wrong.
d We're all going on our summer
holiday.
e She'll get lost if she's not careful.
f The children aren't looking where
they're going.
g You mustn't run across a busy
road.
h I couldn't find my keys which I'd
hidden.
i Where's the buried treasure?
j We've got to go now or we'll be
late.

Unit 15: Revising singular and plural (page 49)

1
a halves   b potatoes   c shelves
d heroes   e loaves   f thieves
g tomatoes   h knives   i leaves
j volcanoes   k calves   l echoes

2
a wolves   b leaves   c loaves
d potatoes   e thieves   f heroes
g shelves   h tomatoes   i halves
j volcanoes

Unit 16: Using personal pronouns (page 50)

1
a b (m e) c d (t h e m)
m n (u s) j k l (y o u)
(h i m) z x c (s h e) k
b v c (h e) p d (i t) a
p (t h e y) q (w e) z x

2
a The boy ran after the ball and kicked it (the ball).
b Emma had a dog. She (Emma) took it (the dog) everywhere.
c "I (Joe) like football," Joe said.
d "Come with us (Amy and Grace)," Amy and Grace said.
e The man wanted the car but it (the car) was too dear for him (the man).
f The children played with the toys but they (the toys) were broken.
g "Are you (Tara and Anna) ready?" Mrs Jones asked Tara and Anna.
h When the dog saw the burglar, it (the dog) chased him (the burglar).

Unit 17: Subject and verb agreement (page 51)

1
a is   b are   c is   d are
e is   f are   g Is   h Are

2
a A panda **has** a round face with small ears.
b Pandas **spend** ten hours a day asleep.
c The cat and the dog **were** great friends.
d Each of the girls **has** a toy.
e Every child **is** ready.
f Neither of the children **was** singing.
g Everybody **was** delighted.
h None of the ships **was** sunk.
i **Is** your friend coming?
j Not one of the children **has** a pencil.

Unit 18: Revising conjunctions (page 52)

1
a It was difficult to see **because** it was so dark.
b You will hurt yourself **if** you fall off your bike.
c I drank a lot of water **because** I was thirsty.
d My brother was pleased **when** I gave him a present.
e It was freezing **so** I put on my coat.
f The door has been broken **since** I slammed it.
g I looked at the clock **but** it had stopped.
h I did my homework early **so** I could watch television.

2 Children's own answers.
Ensure the conjunction in each sentence is underlined:
a because
b since
c when
d although
e if
f so
g where

Unit 19: Revising synonyms (page 53)

1
  a <u>smile</u> <u>grin</u>   b <u>crash</u> <u>smash</u>
  c <u>speak</u> <u>talk</u>   d <u>pull</u> <u>drag</u>
  e <u>cut</u> <u>slit</u>   f <u>cook</u> <u>bake</u>
  g <u>listen</u> <u>hear</u>   h <u>watch</u> <u>look</u>

2

squash	eat	shine	grip	knock
squeeze	consume	glow	hold	bang
crush	swallow	sparkle	grab	hit

Unit 20: Revising speech marks (page 54)

a The teacher asked, "Why are you late?"

b Emma said, "My pet rabbit has escaped."

c Mr Dean shouted, "Keep off my garden!"

d Mrs James said, "It is time to go home."

e Tom said, "Can you help me do my jigsaw?"

f Sharon said, "Bananas are my favourite fruit."

g The driver asked, "How far is it to London?"

h The pirate shouted, "Tell me where you have hidden the gold!"

i Uncle John exclaimed, "What a lovely surprise!"

j The doctor asked, "What is the matter?"

Test 1 (pages 55 and 56)

1 a Stop shouting!   b How lovely!

2 a p**ur**se   b cl**ou**d

3 a a <u>bunch</u> of bananas
    b a <u>pile</u> of stones

4 a The bird, a yellow budgie, flapped its wings.

b Both jumpers, the green and the blue one, were mine.

5 a Some people snore in bed.
    b I put the apple core in the bin.

6 a cupboard   b rainbow

7 a Have you ever <u>seen</u> a ghost?
    b The boy <u>caught</u> a cold.

8 a because   b terrible

9 a <u>sort</u>   <u>taught</u>
    b <u>home</u>   <u>roam</u>

10 a **ex**port   b **mis**judge

Test 2 (pages 57 and 58)

1 a light   b cheap

2 a listen   b talk

3 a stony   b spotty

4 a **We are** going shopping.
    b I **could not** do it.

5 a lots of **leaves** b a sack of **potatoes**

6 a Amy loves to read when <u>she</u> (<u>Amy</u>) is in bed.
    b The dog got muddy when <u>it</u> (<u>the dog</u>) rolled in a puddle.

7 a Each of the apples **is** green.
    b None of the bananas **was** ripe.

8 a You will cry **if** you bang your thumb.
    b I picked up the phone **when** it rang.

9 a <u>cry</u> <u>sob</u>   b <u>run</u> <u>race</u>

10 a The teacher said, "Get out your books."
    b The child asked, "Is it time to go home?"